Englisch als 2. Fremdsprache

W0270189

A1

English G 21

Workbook

Worksheets 1–27

Lösungen zu dem Workbook

Cornelsen

1 Worksheet Hello

1 Funny numbers 🎧1 ✎

Listen. Write down the numbers. / Hör zu und schreibe die richtigen Zahlen auf.

______ ______ ______ ______ ______ ______ ______ ______ ______ ______

______ ______

2 Parrots and colours 🎧3

Listen. Colour the parrots with the right colours. / Hör zu und male die Papageien mit den richtigen Farben aus.

3 Numbers 1–12

Join the numbers: 1 = one, 2 = ... Use a different colour for every number. /
Verbinde die Zahlen: 1 = one, 2 = ... Gib jeder Zahl eine andere Farbe.

10 twelve 3 8 12 ten
nine 1 five 2 three 6
two seven six 5 eight
eleven 4 one 11 7 four 9

1 British boys and girls

Listen. Complete the chart. / Hör zu und fülle die Tabelle aus.

Name	How old?	Where from?
Ben		
*Jes*__________		
*E*__________		
*O*__________		

2 Hi!

Complete the speech bubbles. / Was sagen die Kinder? Fülle die Sprechblasen aus.

3 Dialogues

a) *Cut out the dialogues. Put them in the right order. / Schneide die Dialoge aus. Bringe sie in die richtige Reihenfolge.*

Eleven. What about you?	Where are you from, Jessica?
From London. And you?	Jessica. What about you?
Hello, Ben. I'm Emma.	**Hello. What's your name?**
Hi, my name is Ben. What's your name?	Hi, Oliver.
How old are you, Emma?	I'm Oliver.
I'm from Manchester.	Oh, I'm from London too.
I'm ten. Where are you from, Ben?	London.

b) *Check with your partner. / Überprüfe die Dialoge zusammen mit deinem Partner/deiner Partnerin.*

1 You and I and he and she ✎

Join the right circles and complete the list. / Verbinde die richtigen Kreise mit Linien. Schreibe dann die Liste rechts zu Ende.

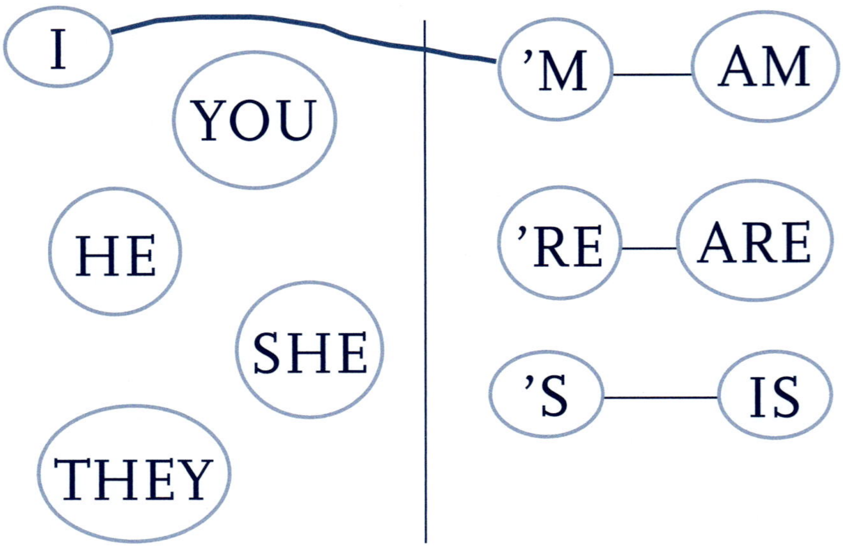

I’m – I am

You’ ______ – ______ ______

H______ – ____ ____

S______ – _____ _____

T__________ – _______ _______

2 This is … ✎

Write about the boys and girls from Bristol. / Stelle die Jungen und Mädchen aus Bristol vor.

This is Ananda. She’s eleven years old. She’s from Bristol.

________ ____ Dan. He’s ____________ __________ ______.

He’s from ______________ too.

________ ____ Jack. ________ ____________ __________ ______.

He’s ________ ______________.

________ ____ J___. ________ ____________ __________ ______.

________ ________ Bristol ______.

________ ____ S_________. _________ __________ _________ ______.

She’s new in ______________.

1 Match to the pictures 🎧 7

a) *Listen. Match the right letter to the pictures. / Hör zu und schreibe den richtigen Buchstaben (a, b, c, d, e) zu jedem Bild.*

___

___

___

___

___

b) *Complete the sentences with the right verbs. / Vervollständige die Sätzen mit den richtigen Verben aus der Liste.* ✎

1 I can __________ the house.

2 I can't __________ the door.

3 __________ it. Don't __________ it.

4 Can I __________ the window, please?

5 __________ the door, please.

6 I can't __________ my skateboard.

close
open
push
pull
see
find

2 Words ✎

Join the dots and label the pictures. / Verbinde die Zahlen in den Zeichnungen. Schreibe das richtige Wort zu jedem Bild.

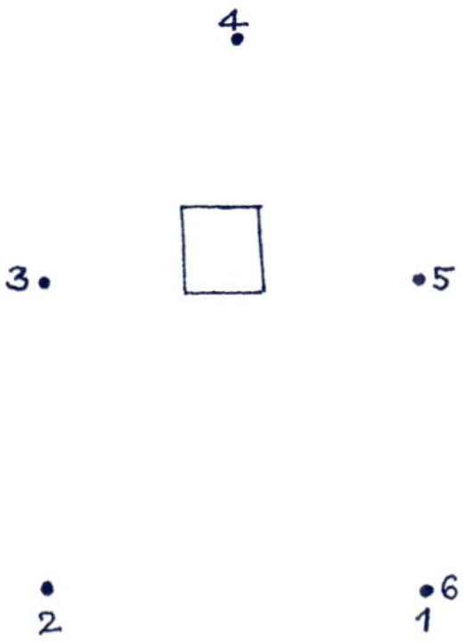
____

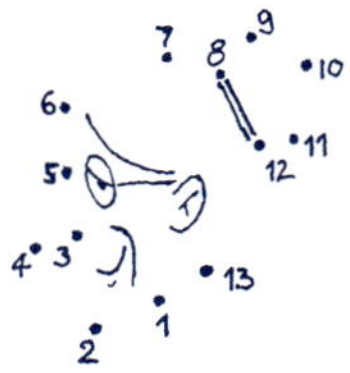
____

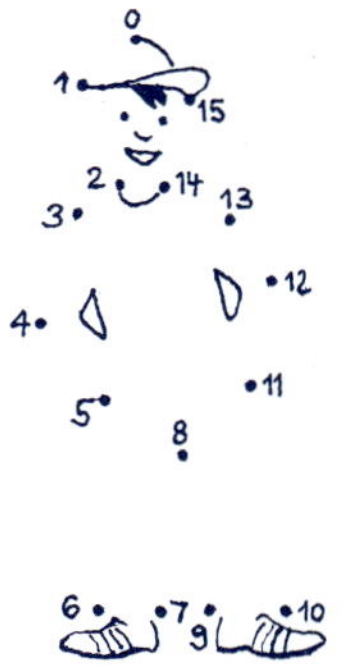
____

____

boy
house
laugh
old

1 Who is missing? ✎

Look at page 11 in your book. Who's missing in the house? Write their names in the house. / Sieh dir die Bilder auf Seite 11 des Buches an. Wer fehlt im Haus in Cotham Park Road? Schreibe ihre Namen ins Haus.

2 Who says what? 🎧 8

Listen. Match the right names to the sentences. / Hör zu. Wer sagt was? Schreibe den richtigen Namen zu den Aussagen.

1 You can take baby Hannah.
Mrs Carter-Brown

2 I can take the dog, Mum.
____

3 And Toby, you go with Emily.
____

4 But Dad, where is my room?
____

5 Where's your mother's plan?
____

6 Let's be friends.
____

3 Right or wrong? 🎧 8

Listen again. Are the sentences right (✓) or wrong (✖)? / Hör nochmals zu. Sind die Aussagen richtig (✓) oder falsch (✖)?

1 Toby is with Emily. ✓

2 Hannah is with Emily. ___

3 Sheeba is with Sophie's dad. ___

4 Sophie's room is nice. ___

5 Sophie can't see Prunella. ___

6 Sophie and Prunella are friends. ___

4 Song: Friday I'm in love 🎧 9

Listen to the song and sing along. / Hör dir das Lied an und singe mit.

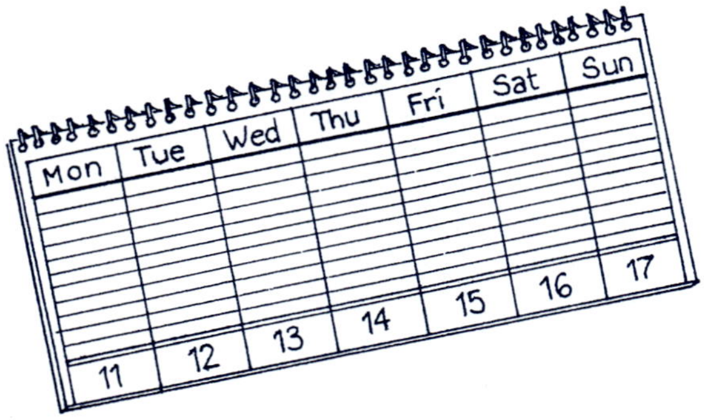

I don't care if Monday's blue
Tuesday's grey and Wednesday too
Thursday I don't care about you
It's Friday I'm in love.

Saturday wait
And Sunday always comes too late
But Friday never hesitate ...

Monday you can fall apart
Tuesday, Wednesday break my heart
Thursday doesn't even start
It's Friday I'm in love.

The Cure

1 Address and telephone number 🎧 10

Listen and write down the numbers. / Hör zu und schreibe die Zahlen auf.

Address: 27 Wood Road.
Phone: ____________
Mobile: ____________
____

Address: ___ Bell Road.
Phone: ____________
Mobile: ____________
____

Address: ___ Church Street.
Phone: ____________
Mobile: ____________
____

Address: ___ Bell Road.
Phone: ____________
Mobile: ____________
____

2 Good luck! ✂ 🎧 11

a) *Cut out the dialogue. Put it in the right order. Then listen and check. / Schneide den Dialog aus. Bringe ihn in die richtige Reihenfolge. Dann hör zu, ob du ihn richtig hast.*

Mrs Schmidt: Excuse me, can I say goodbye?	Polly: Good luck! Good luck.
Mrs Schmidt: Your B&B is great. Thank you, Mr Hanson, and goodbye.	Mrs Schmidt: Goodbye, Polly. And goodbye, Jack.
Jack: Goodbye ... and a nice trip back to Germany, Mrs Schmidt.	Mrs Schmidt: Thank you Jack. And good luck with your new school.
Mr Hanson: Oh, Mrs Schmidt ...	Polly: Goodbye. Goodbye.
	Mr Hanson: Thank you, Mrs Schmidt.

b) *Complete the dialogues with phrases from the box. / Vervollständige die Dialoge mit Redewendungen aus dem Kasten.*

Excuse me
Goodbye
Good luck
Good morning
Thank you

MRS SCHMIDT: Good morning, Jack,
JACK: Oh, ____________
____________, Mrs Schmidt.
MRS SCHMIDT: Is it your first day at school today?
JACK: Yes, my new school.
MRS SCHMIDT: Well, ____________, Jack.
JACK: ____________, Mrs Schmidt.

MRS SCHMIDT: ____________, Mr Hanson.
MR HANSON: Oh, hello, Mrs Schmidt.
MRS SCHMIDT: Can I say ____________?
MR HANSON: Oh, yes, ____________, Mrs Schmidt. And a nice trip back to Germany.
MRS SCHMIDT: ____________, Mr Hanson. And
____________, Polly.
POLLY: ____________

1 Word and picture puzzle ✎ ✂

a) *Write one word from the box on the right on each card (1–14). Then draw a picture of the word on the card next to it.* / *Schreibe ein Wort aus dem Kasten auf jede Karte (1–14) und zeichne das Wort auf die Karte daneben.*

b) *Before you cut out the cards draw one big person or animal from your English book on the back of the whole page.* / *Bevor Du die Karten ausschneidest, zeichne eine Person oder ein Tier aus deinem Englischbuch auf die gesamte Rückseite.*

c) *Cut out your cards and swap them with a partner. Can you put your partner's cards together in the right order? What is the drawing on the back?* / *Schneide deine Karten aus und tausche sie mit deinem Partner/deiner Partnerin. Kannst du seine/ihre Karten wieder richtig zusammenfügen? Was hat er/sie auf der Rückseite gemalt?*

apple • book • CD • chair • milk • mobile phone • money • pen • pencil • ruler • rubber • table • tea • toast

1 apple		8	
2		9	
3		10	
4		11	
5		12	
6		13	
7		14	

1 Monsters 🎧 12 ✎

Listen. What do the monsters say? Write it down. / Hör zu. Was sagen die Monster? Schreibe es auf.

YOU'RE
I'M
SHE'S
THEY'RE
HE'S
WE'RE
IT'S

2 I'm a monster ✎

Answer the questions. / Beantworte die Fragen.

1 I'm a monster. Are you a monster too? – *No, I'm not.*

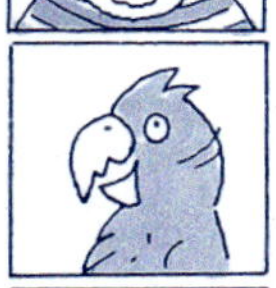

2 Is Polly a parrot? – ______________

3 Are you a parrot? – ______________

4 Is Emma a boy? – ______________

Now you:

5 Is your partner a boy? – ______________

____

6 Are you friends? – ______________

7 Are your friends in your class? – ______

____

1 Can you do it too? ✎

Complete the sentences and questions. Answer the questions. /
Vervollständige die Aussagen und Fragen. Beantworte die Fragen.

1 I can sing a song. Can you sing a song too? – ______________________

2 I ______ talk to my mum in English. ______ you talk to your mum in English too? – ______________

3 I ______ ________ football. ______ you ________ football too? – ______________________

4 I ______ ____________ to music. ______ ______ ____________ to music too? – ______________

5 I ______ ________ the door. ______ ______ ________ the door too? – ______________________

6 I ______ ______ 'Good morning' in German. ______ ______ ______ 'Good morning' in German too? –

____

7 I ______ ______ bananas. ______ ______ ______ ______________ too? – ______________

8 I ______ __________ trees. ______ ______ __________ __________ too? – ______________

2 What can they play? 🎧 13 ✎

a) Listen and fill in the chart.
They can play it = ✔. They can't play it = ✘.
You don't know = ? /
Hör zu und fülle die Tabelle aus.
Sie können es spielen = ✔. Sie können es nicht spielen = ✘. Du weißt es nicht = ?

b) Write about the children in your exercise book. / Schreibe über die Kinder in dein Heft.
Oliver can play football. He can't play tennis. Maybe he can play badminton and basketball. I don't know.

Name	Football	Badminton	Basketball	Tennis
Oliver				
Emma				
Jessica				
Ben				

1 Monster card game ✂

Cut out the monster cards and play Happy Families. / Schneidet die Monster-Karten aus und spielt Quartett.

A: Have you got Jag/Mrs Jag/Brok/Sok/the monster cat/the monster dog/the monster fish/ the monster bird?

B: Yes, I have. Here you are. / No, I haven't. My turn.

1 In the classroom

What are the people in the pictures saying? Find the right answers in the green box on page 28 of your English book. Write them under the pictures. / Was sagen die Leute auf den Bildern? Finde die Antworten im grünen Kasten auf Seite 28 deines Englischbuches und schreibe sie unter die Bilder.

2 Hi there

a) *Cut out the dialogue and put it in the right order. / Schneide den Dialog aus und bringe ihn in die richtige Reihenfolge.*

Alex:	Hi, I'm Alex.
Alex:	Hi Linda.
Alex:	Crazy but great!
Linda:	Do you like basketball, Alex?
Alex:	OK. But what's your name?
Linda:	Oh, hello, Alex. Let's sit together.
Linda:	Oh, sorry. I'm Linda.
Alex:	Yes, I love basketball. And ice hockey.
Linda:	Ice hockey? Ice hockey is crazy!

b) *Complete the dialogue. / Vervollständige den Dialog.*

A: Hi there, I'm Jan.

You: ______________________

A: Do you like football?

You: ______________________

A: Let's sit together and watch the game.

You: ______________________

A: What's your favourite subject at school?

You: ______________________

A: Yes, I like that too. And maths.

You: ______________________

1 Class birthdays 14

a) Write the names of the months in English in the birthday wheel. / Schreibe die Monatsnamen auf Englisch ins Geburtstagsrad.

b) Listen and write down the number of birthdays in the class for each month in the birthday wheel. / Hör zu und schreibe die Anzahl der Geburtstage für jeden Monat ins Geburtstagsrad.

c) Listen again and write down the birthdays of one student in each month. / Hör ein zweites Mal zu und trage für jeden Monat den Geburtstag eines Schülers oder einer Schülerin ein.

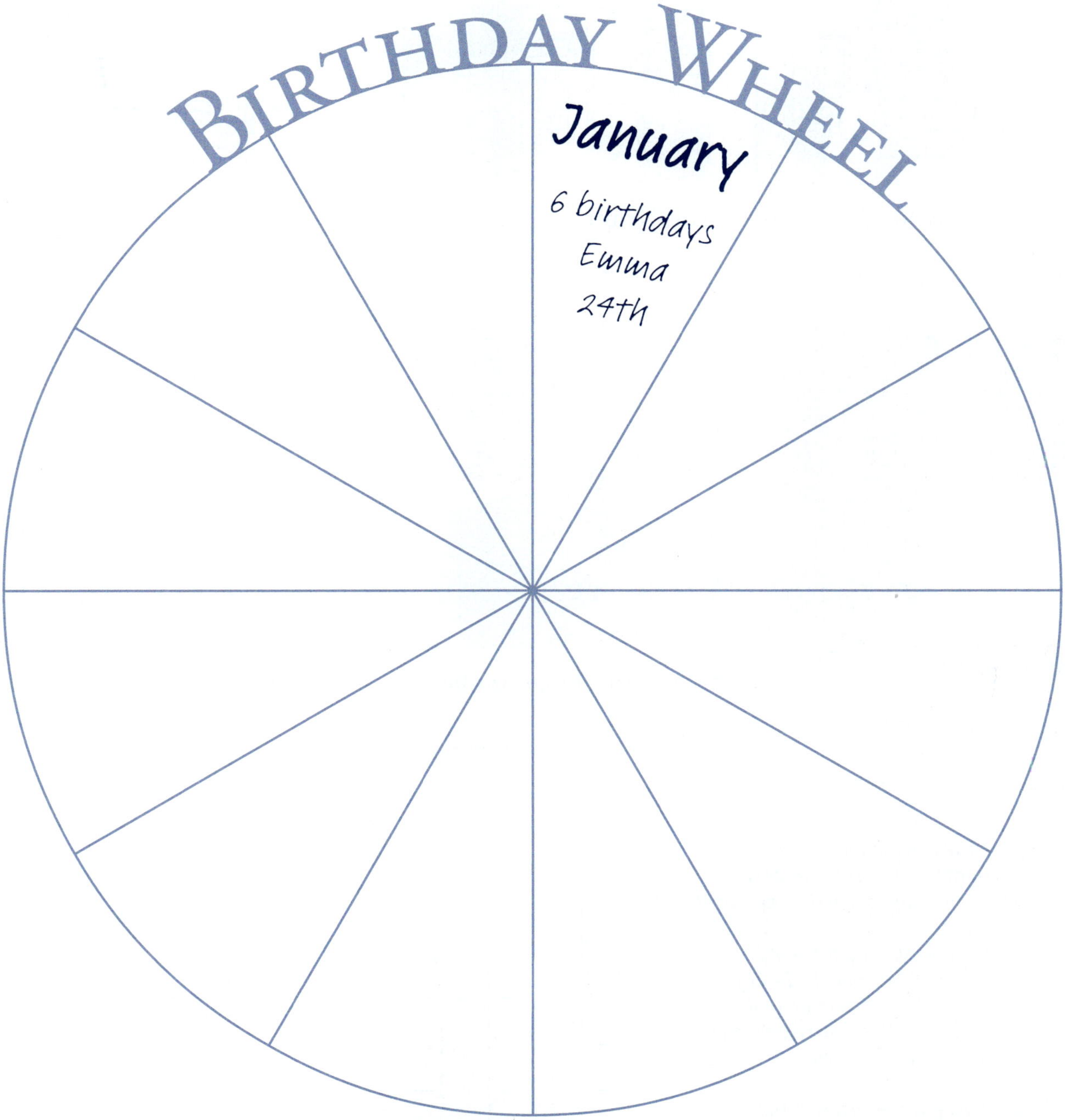

You write	*You say*
24th January My birthday is on 24th January, 2001.	**the** twenty-fourth **of** January My birthday is on **the** twenty-fourth **of** January, two thousand and one.

1 Ben at home ✎

a) Look at the pictures of Ben's house and room. Complete the words under the pictures. / Sieh dir die Bilder von Bens Haus und Zimmer an. Vervollständige die Wörter darunter.

Hi, I'm Ben. I live in a f______ 6↓ in this big h________. 4↓

This is my r______. 7↓

We've got a nice g__________. 2↓

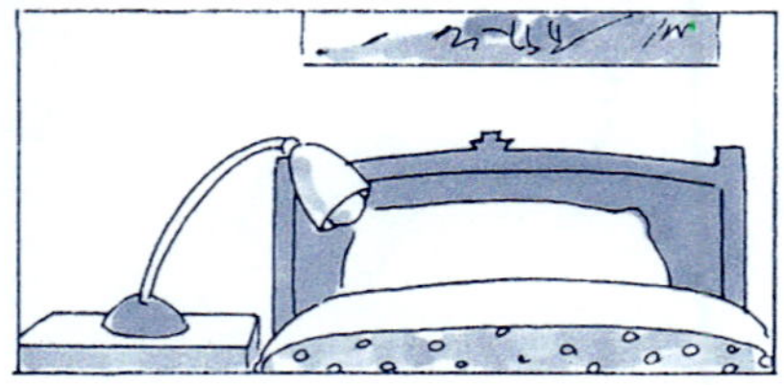

I can read in b____ 4→ with this l_____. 3→

Here are all the books on the s________ 1→ next to my w______________. 2→

My favourite things: my big d______ 5↓, my old c________ 1↓ and my c______________. 3↓

b) Have you got all the words right? Look at the numbers (1↓ etc.) and fill in the crossword puzzle. / Hast du alle Wörter richtig geschrieben? Sieh dir die Ziffer neben den Wörtern an und fülle dann das Kreuzworträtsel mit den Wörtern aus.

c) Now put the letters in the circles in the right order and make a sentence. / Bringe die Buchstaben in den Kreisen in die richtige Reihenfolge und bilde einen Satz.

________ ___ ___ ________.

1 Who lives there? 15 ✎

Listen and write the right name – Ben, Emma, Jessica, Oliver – under the houses and flats. / Hör zu und schreibe die richtigen Namen – Ben, Emma, Jessica, Oliver – unter die Häuser und Wohnungen.

____

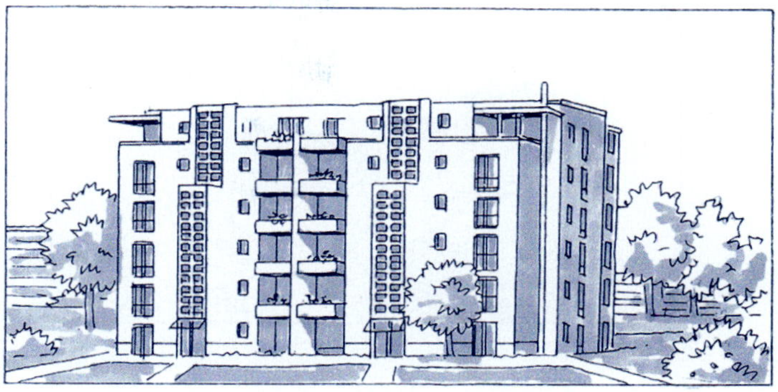

____

____

____

2 Pets sleep in a …? ✎

Where are the pets? Is that right or wrong? Write in your exercise book. / Wo sind die Haustiere? Ist das richtig oder falsch? Schreibe es in dein Heft.

… sleep in a/an … | basket. / cage. / hutch. / aquarium.

That's right.
That's wrong. … sleep in …

Cats sleep in an aquarium. That's wrong. Cats sleep in a basket.

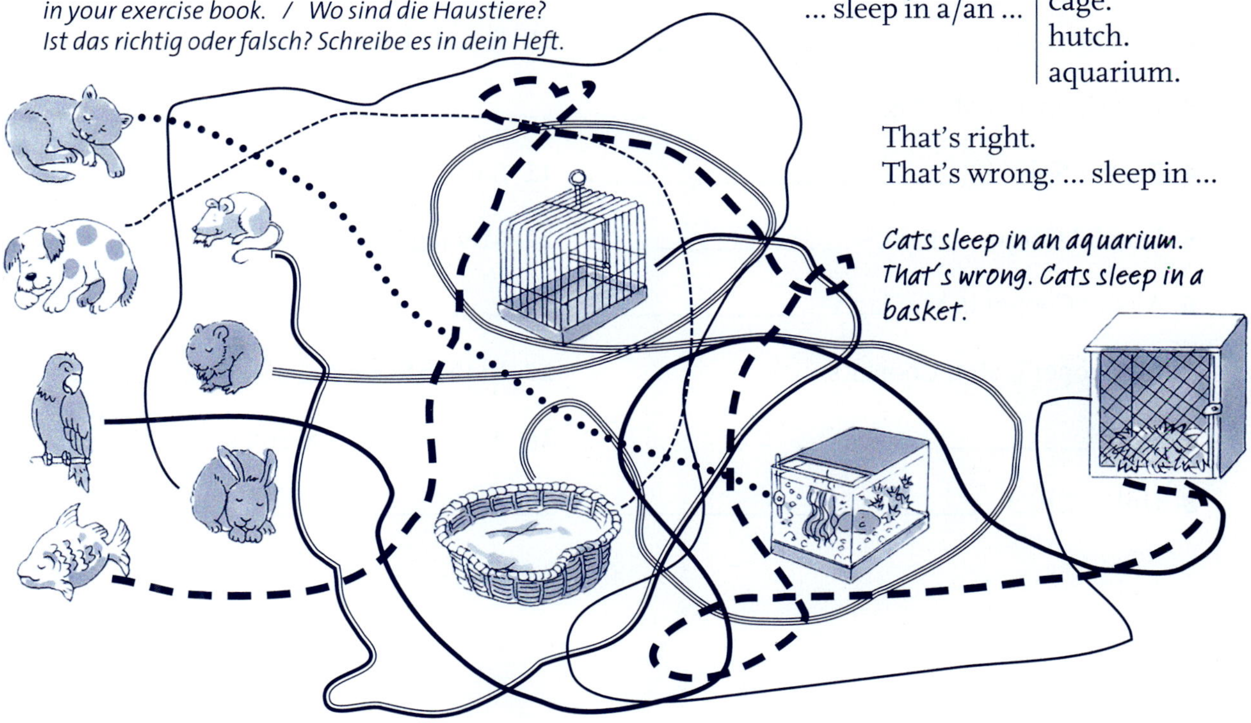

15 Worksheet Unit 2

1 Meet the Monsters ✎

a) Look at the Monsters' family tree. Then complete the sentences with the right word. / Sieh dir den Familienstammbaum der Monster an. Dann vervollständige die Sätze mit dem richtigen Wort.

1 Jagar is Sok's ______________________.

2 Unk is Brok's ______________________.

3 Ron Cooper is Mrs Jag's ______________.

4 Brok is Sok's ______________________.

5 Donald Cooper is Brok's ______________.

6 Alison Cooper is Mrs Jag's ____________.

7 Jill Cooper is Ron Cooper's

______________________.

8 Unk is Jiffi's ______________________.

9 Jag is Brok's ______________________.

10 Brok is Lana Cooper's

______________________.

11 Sok is Jagar's ______________________.

12 Mrs Jag is Donald Cooper's

______________________.

13 Klob is Sok's ______________________.

14 Alison Cooper is Sok's

______________________.

1 Who are they? 16

a) Who likes what? Listen and write their names in the empty faces: Oliver, Jessica, Jessica's sister, Oliver's mother. / Wer mag was? Hör Oliver und Jessica zu und schreibe ihre Namen in die leeren Gesichter: Oliver, Jessica, Jessicas Schwester, Olivers Mutter.

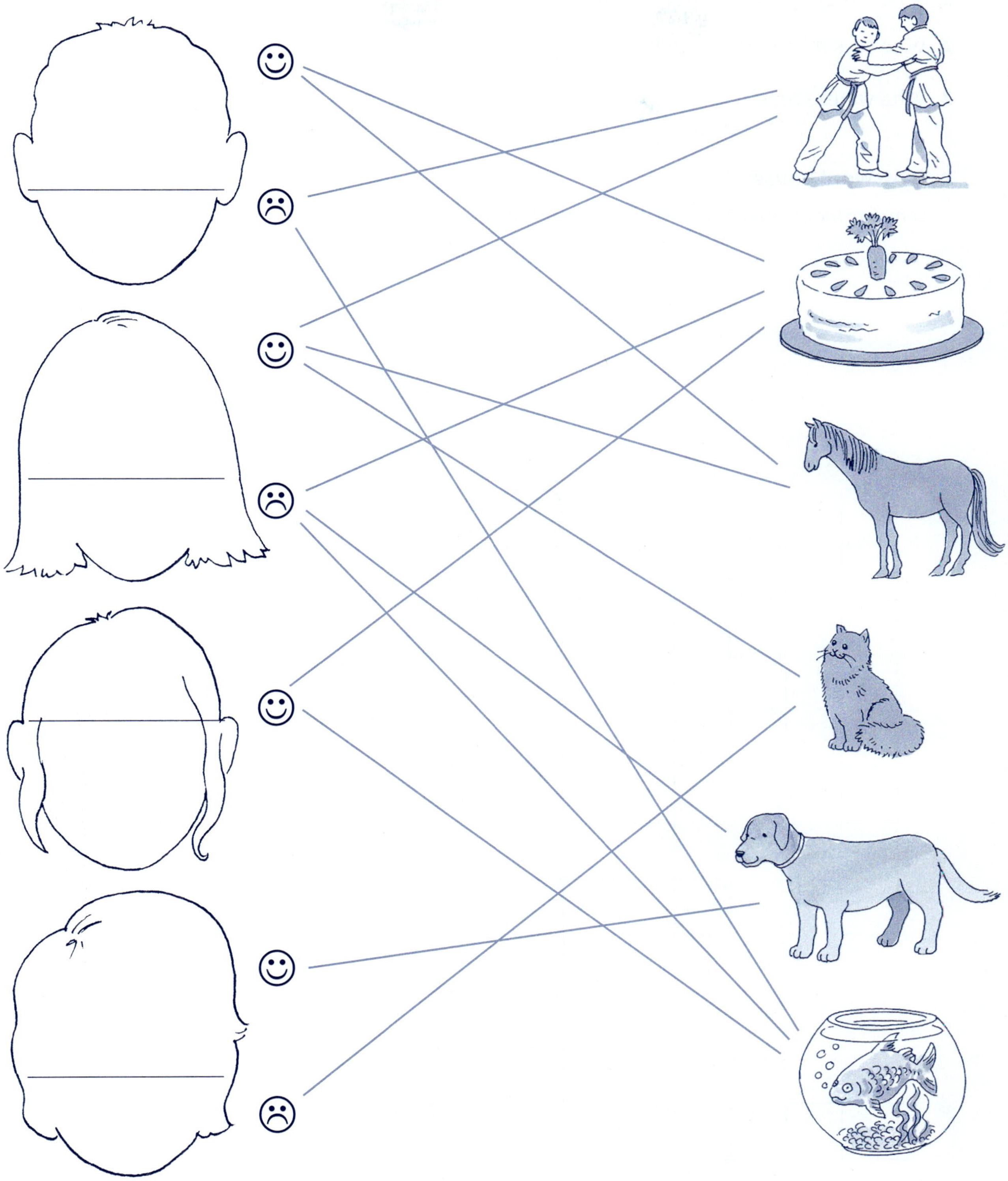

b) Write three sentences like this for your partner. Ask him/her: are they right or wrong? / Schreibe drei Sätze und frage deinen Partner/deine Partnerin, ob sie richtig oder falsch sind.

You: Jessica likes carrot cake, but she doesn't like judo. Right or wrong?

Your partner: That's right. / That's wrong.

17 Worksheet Unit 2

1 Monster dinner 17

Listen and answer the questions. / Hör zu und beantworte die Fragen.

1 Who has got plans for this evening? ______________________

2 Who says it's monster fish for dinner? ______________________

3 Who wants chips? ______________________

2 Crossword house

Complete the crossword. / Löse das Kreuzworträtsel.

Across

3 The rooms at the top of the house are ...

6 You put water in this and wash the dishes.

9 You sit and eat your food here.

10 This washes the dishes for you.

11 The rooms at the bottom of the house are ...

Down

1 You keep things like cups and plates in this.

2 This keeps things cold.

4 Two or three people can sit on this. It's comfortable.

5 Like 4 down, but for one person.

7 You cook food in this room.

8 You sleep in this.

12 You watch films and other things on this.

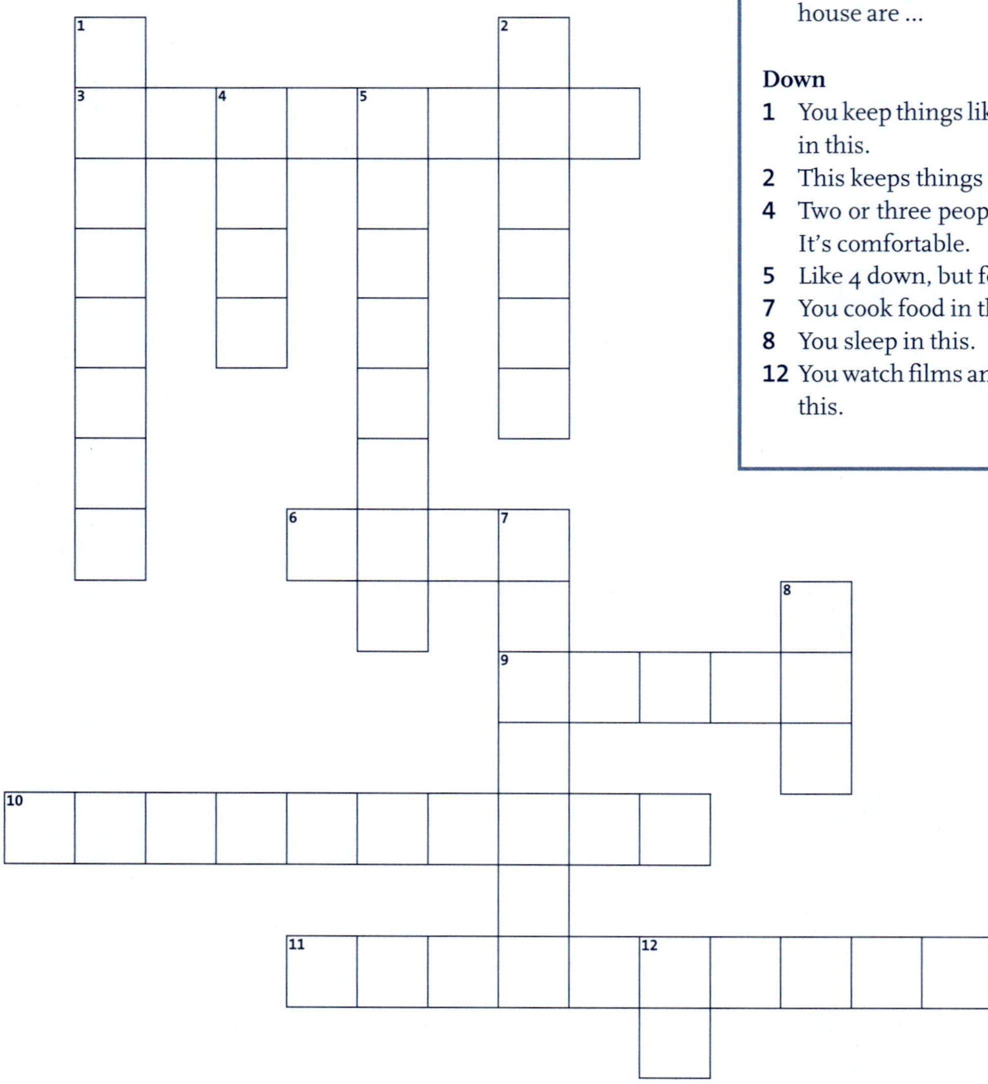

1 Hobbies ✎

Look at the pictures and write about the children's hobbies. Choose the right verbs and nouns from the boxes. / Sieh dir die Bilder an und schreibe über die Hobbys der Kinder. Verwende die richtigen Verben und Nomen aus den Kästen.

collect • go • go to • listen to • phone • play • watch

football • friends • judo lessons • music • riding • skiing • stamps • swimming • tennis • TV

Ben ____________ stamps. He ________ ____________ and he ________ ____________.

Emma ________ tennis. She ________ ____________ and she ____________ ____.

Jessica ________ ____________. She ________ ____________ and she ____________ ____ ________.

Oliver ________ ____________. He ________ ____ ________ ____________ and he ____________ ____________.

2 When? ✎

The letters under the pictures are mixed up time phrases. Can you correct them? / Die Zeitbegriffe unter den Bildern sind durcheinandergekommen. Kannst du sie richtig aufschreiben?

ATFRE LSHCOO

________ ____________

IN HET IRONGMN

____ ____ ____________

NO NAEDDSYWSE

____ ____________

TA GNTIH

____ ________

NO ODYMANS

____ ____________

TA ETH DENKEWE

____ ______ ________

Worksheet Unit 3

1 Monster poems ✎

Write more poems for the other pictures. / Schreibe Gedichte zu den anderen Bildern.

In the morning I play football,
I play football in the afternoon.
In the evening I play football,
I play football all day long.

1 Lazy Larry 18

a) Listen to Lazy Larry. In what order does he do the things in the pictures? Give each picture the right number from 1 to 7. / Hör Lazy Larry zu. In welcher Reihenfolge tut er die Dinge, die man auf den Bildern sieht? Gib jedem Bild die richtige Zahl von 1 bis 7.

b) Now write what Lazy Larry does. / Schreibe jetzt, was Lazy Larry tut.

1 First Lazy Larry drinks his tea.

2 Then he __________ his book.

3 Then _____ __________ his apple.

4 ________ _____ ________ his apple.

5 ________ _____ ____________ his shopping list.

6 ________ _____ ____________ _______ friend.

7 ________ _____ ____________ _____.

2 Football on the radio 19

Listen and colour the two players in the right colours. Which team is winning? Cross out the other team. / Hör zu und male die zwei Spieler in den richtigen Farben aus. Wer führt? Streiche die andere Mannschaft durch.

United City are winning.

3 German–English sports dictionary 20

Lots of English and German sports words are almost the same. But how do you say them in English? Match the German to the English words and the right pronunciation. Then listen to the CD. / Viele englische und deutsche Sportbegriffe sind einander sehr ähnlich. Aber wie spricht man sie auf Englisch aus? Ordne die deutschen Begriffe den englischen Wörtern und ihrer Aussprache zu. Höre danach die CD.

Arena	pass	[net]
Ball	arena	[bɔːl]
Foul	set	[set]
Netz	net	[pɑːs]
Pass	foul	[pɔɪnt]
Punkt	point	[faʊl]
Satz	volley	['vɒli]
Volley	ball	[ə'riːnə]

1 Who buys what? 21

Listen to the CD. Who buys what? Write the right names under the pictures – Ben, Emma, Jessica and Oliver. / Hör dir die CD an. Wer kauft was? Schreibe die richtigen Namen unter die Bilder – Ben, Emma, Jessica und Oliver.

  ☐ 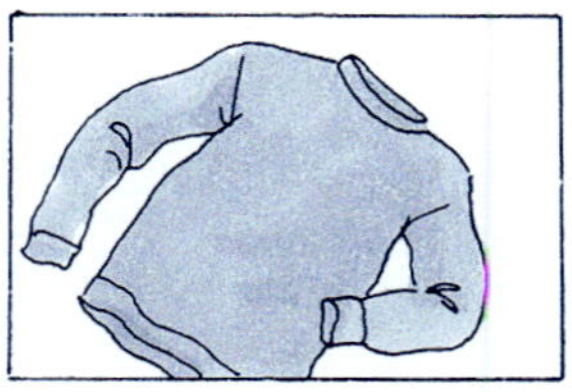

__________ __________ __________ __________

2 How much is that? 22

a) *Write down how much money is in the pictures. / Schreibe auf, wie viel Geld du auf den Bildern siehst.*

☐

*Twenty-*__________ __________

__________ p

☐

__________ __________ __________ ___

☐

__________ __________

__________ – __________ ___

b) *Listen to the three dialogues and give each picture the right number (1, 2 or 3) in the little boxes. / Hör dir die drei Dialoge an und schreibe bei jedem Bild die richtige Zahl (1, 2, oder 3) in das Kästchen.*

1 Favourite party food and drink ✎

What's their favourite party food and drink? Write it down. / Schreibe auf, was sie am liebsten auf einer Party essen und trinken.

Emma's favourite party food is f________ s________. Her favourite drink is t____.

Ben's favourite p________ f______ is c________. His f________________ d________ is ________.

Brok's f________________ __________ ________ is m____________ f______. His ____________________ __________ is ________________.

Sok's f______________ __________ ________ is U________ C__________. Her ________________ __________ is ____________ ________.

2 At the monster party 🎧 23 ✎

Listen to the CD. Who wants what? Write the right names under the pictures. / Wer möchte was? Hör zu und schreibe die richtigen Namen unter die Bilder.

________________________ ________________________

1 A present for Jessica ✎

It's Jessica's birthday. What do her friends want to give her? Use the phrases in the box and complete the dialogue. / Was wollen Jessicas Freunde ihr zum Geburtstag schenken? Vervollständige den Dialog mit den Wendungen aus dem Kasten.

Do you know? • I don't know. • I know. • Let's buy/get ... • ... likes ... • No, I don't. • No, that's boring • That's a good idea. • What about ...? • What ... does she like?

Ben: I know a present for Jessica. L________ _______ her some soap.

Emma: ________? No, that's _____________. W_______ __________ a _____?

Oliver: T__________ __ _________ _________. What __________ d______ ______ ________?

Ben: I d________ _________. Emma, do ______ _________?

Emma: N__ , __ ___________.

Ben: Oh. Well, w______ ___________ a _________________.
Jessica l_________ _________________.

Oliver: Yes, t__________ __ _________ _________. L_________ ______ her __ _________________.

Emma: OK.

2 A present for Sok 🎧 24

It's Sok's birthday too. Listen to the CD. What presents does she get? Write them down. / Auch Sok hat Geburtstag. Hör zu und schreibe auf, welche Geschenke sie bekommt.

__ _________ __ ______________ _________ from her mum and __ ______________ ___________ from her dad.

1 At school ✎

Find 14 school words in the word box and write them down on the right. / Finde 14 Schulwörter im Wortkasten und schreibe sie rechts auf.

W	O	U	B	T	U	W	N	S	U	Y	N
B	P	S	D	B	H	G	L	T	G	V	W
R	L	F	A	J	A	D	K	U	B	R	A
T	T	W	R	K	B	S	Z	D	X	S	Q
E	N	G	L	I	S	H	X	E	C	T	I
A	Z	E	L	E	S	S	O	N	P	I	O
C	S	O	H	F	R	A	F	T	R	M	M
H	B	G	J	D	L	B	R	U	L	E	R
E	K	R	T	E	B	R	E	A	K	T	K
R	O	A	W	X	L	U	N	C	H	A	L
X	I	P	E	N	T	G	C	L	U	B	P
M	M	H	Q	M	A	T	H	S	C	L	W
O	L	Y	P	S	C	I	E	N	C	E	A

P	E	N						
T	E	A	C	H	E	R		

2 Monster timetable 🎧 25 ✎

a) *Brok and Sok go to Monster School. Listen and complete their timetable. / Brok und Sok gehen in die Monsterschule. Hör zu und vervollständige ihren Stundenplan.*

MONSTER SCHOOL TIMETABLE

Time	Subject	Teacher
10 – 10.30	Monster b ______	
10.35 – ______	______ ______	______
______ – 11.10	______ ______	______
11.10 – 12.10	______ ______	
12.15 – ______	______ ______	______
2.35	End of school. Monster children ____ ______.	

Mr Growl

Mrs Grimm

Mr Grabble

b) *Compare with your partner. / Vergleiche mit deinem Partner/deiner Partnerin.*

c) *Listen again and check. / Hör nochmals zu und überprüfe den Stundenplan.*

25 Worksheet Unit 5

1 That was great!

You want to say the following in English. Choose the right English phrases from the list and write them down. / Du willst Folgendes auf Englisch sagen. Wähle die richtigen englischen Wendungen aus der Liste und schreibe sie hin.

- ***Everybody loved it.***
- ***How was the show?***
- ***I really liked it.***
- ***That was great.***
- ***The music was boring.***
- ***The show was all right.***
- ***You look fantastic.***
- ***You're a great dancer.***

1 Du willst sagen, dass etwas großartig war.

____

2 Du willst sagen, dass die Show OK war.

____

3 Du willst sagen, dass die Musik langweilig war.

____

4 Du willst sagen, dass es jedem gefallen hat.

____

5 Du willst sagen, dass du es sehr gut fandest.

____

6 Du willst fragen, wie die Show war.

____

7 Du willst jemandem sagen, dass er/sie großartig tanzen kann.

____

8 Du willst jemandem sagen, dass er/sie fantastisch aussieht.

____

2 Jokes 26

a) *Look at the picture and write the joke down in the right order. / Sieh dir das Bild an und schreibe den Witz in der richtigen Reihenfolge auf.*

Boy: It keeps the tigers away.

Boy: See?

Girl: There aren't any tigers in England.

Girl: Why are you doing that?

b) *Listen to the CD and fill in the speech bubbles. / Hör zu und fülle die Sprechblasen aus.*

1 In the city ✎

What can you see in the picture? Complete the labels. / Was kannst du auf dem Bild sehen? Beschrifte es richtig.

2 7PK's project 🎧 27 ✎

Listen and complete the sentences. / Hör zu und vervollständige die Sätze.

1 Mr Kingsley talks about photo number ___.

2 The students in form 7PK have to answer these three questions:

____

____

____

3 Groups have to choose ___ places.

4 At Explore-at-Bristol you can see ______________.

5 You can go there by ______, and you can __________ or __________ there.

6 It costs £______ for kids.

1 The presentation 28

Emma, Ben, Oliver and Jessica are doing a project and have to do a presentation. Listen and answer the questions. Put a tick (✔) in the right box. / Emma, Ben, Oliver und Jessica machen ein Projekt und müssen ihre Ergebnisse präsentieren. Hör zu und beantworte die Fragen. Mache ein Häkchen (✔) an die richtige Antwort.

1 What is the project about?
❏ Stuttgart ❏ Hamburg
❏ Berlin ❏ Bristol

2 Where are they going to write their notes?
❏ In an exercise book ❏ On cards
❏ On a piece of paper ❏ On their poster

3 Who is going to talk about the Beatles?
❏ Ben ❏ Emma
❏ Jessica ❏ Oliver

4 Who is going to talk about the football club?
❏ Ben ❏ Emma
❏ Jessica ❏ Oliver

5 Who is going to talk about ships and the harbour?
❏ Ben ❏ Emma
❏ Jessica ❏ Oliver

6 Who is going to start and finish the presentation?
❏ Ben ❏ Emma
❏ Jessica ❏ Oliver

7 Which topic comes first?
❏ The Beatles ❏ The football club
❏ Ships and the harbour

8 Which topic comes last?
❏ The Beatles ❏ The football club
❏ Ships and the harbour

2 Merry Christmas 29

Listen and match scenes 1–5 to the pictures A–E. / Hör zu und ordne die Hörszenen 1–5 den Bildern A–E zu.

3 A Christmas song 30

Listen and sing along. / Hör zu und sing mit.

I saw three ships
I saw three ships come sailing in
on Christmas day, on Christmas day.
I saw three ships come sailing in
on Christmas day in the morning.

And what was in those ships all three
on Christmas day, on Christmas day?
And what was in those ships all three
on Christmas day in the morning?

Our Saviour Christ and his lady
on Christmas day, on Christmas day.
Our Saviour Christ and his lady
on Christmas day in the morning.

1 Hello Emma!

a) *Read and write.* 1 is... 2 ...years 3 `m
4 favourite colour

b) *Write questions.* 1 What's your name?
2 How old are you?
3 Where are you from?
4 What's your favourite colour?

2 New names

a) *Write.* 2 is Ananda. 3 This is Jack.
4 This is Jo. 5 This is Sophie.

b) *Match and write.*
1 She's 11 years old. She's from Bristol.
2 He's 11 years old. He's from Bristol.
3 They're twins. They're 12 years old.
They're from Bristol.
4 She's 11 years old. She's new in Bristol.

Now you

Write about a boy and a girl in your class.
... is–... years old from ...
... is–... years old from ...

3 WORDS What can you see?

a) *Write the correct numbers in the box.*
kite 4 water 2 trees 10 skateboard 8
football 6 house 9 boy 7 girls 3 boys 5

b) *Write the words.* w a t e r g i r l s
k i t e b o y s f o o t b a l l b o y
s k a t e b o a r d h o u s e t r e e s

c) *Write correct words.*
boat football
water skateboard

4 WORDS A word kite

Find and write.
mum dad
push pull
open close
old new
empty full

5 WORDS Dan's school shopping list

a) *Match and write.*
pencil sharpener school bag
exercise book glue stick
pencil case felt tip

6 WORDS Colour words

Find and colour the colour words.
yellow orange black red green pink blue

7 Prunella's plates

What colours are Prunella's plates? Write the colours.
red green pink
brown white purple
yellow orange black

Now you

orange It's red, orange and yellow.
It's blue and green. It's red and white.

8 What day is it?

Write the day. Look at the pictures and Jo's diary.
It's Saturday. It's Tuesday.
It's Friday. It's Thursday.
It's Wednesday. It's Sunday.

9 Find the house numbers

a) *Match six house numbers to the speech bubbles. Write the correct numbers from the box.*
13 17 7
42 24 28

b) *Now write the red house numbers in words.*
fourteen, forty, seventy, fifty-five

10 Who am I?

a) *Read the secret code and write the letters in the speech bubble.*
M Y N A M E I S
B A R N A B A S .
W H A T ' S Y O U R
N A M E ?

b) *Write your answer in code. Write the numbers in words.*
twenty-five thirteen twenty-four
thirty-seven twenty-five thirty-three
twenty-nine nineteen

11 What's the time?

Draw the time on the clocks.
5:25 4:36 12:02

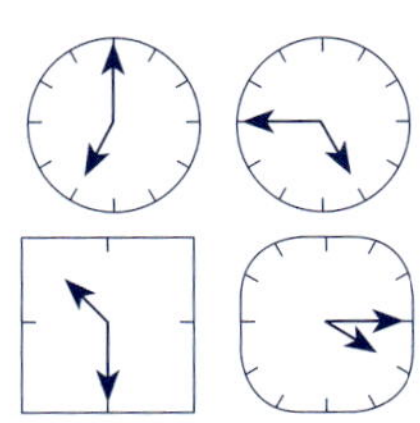

12 Prunella's clocks

Look at Prunella's clocks. Write the times.
1 five o'clock
2 It's half past six.
3 It's twelve o five.
4 It's quarter to three.
5 It's eight twenty-four.
6 It's quarter past eleven.

Clock number five *is right.*

13 WORDS S-words

Read and write.

2 shop 3 sister 4 summer
5 Sunday 6 Saturday 7 skateboard

1 WORDS What's in the picture?

a) *Write the names of the things.*

1 school bag 2 skateboard
3 mobile phone 4 table
5 books 6 felt tips
7 apples 8 glue sticks
9 kites

b) *Make a new word.* b r e a k f a s t

c) *Write sentences with there is or there are.*

2 There's a skateboard.
3 There's a mobile phone.
4 There's a table.

6 There are two felt tips.
7 There are three apples.
8 There are two glue sticks.
9 There are two kites.

2 WORDS Day one

Write words from the boxes.

y e a r
s t u d e n t s
R o o m
t w i n s
n e r v o u s
f i r s t

3 *He, she, it, ...*

Match and colour.

they	he	she	she	she
it	they	he	he	she
she	it	they	he	they
it	it	it	they	he

4 Hello!

Write.

Dan It
Florian he she She We It
Sophie I you
Florian I They
Teacher You It

5 I'm Dan

a) *Complete with short forms.*

1 You're 2 I'm he's
3 She's It's 4 We're 5 They're

b) *What's wrong?*

2 It isn't half past eight. It's half past seven.
3 They aren't at the B&B. They're at school.
4 He isn't in Room 14. He's in Room 16.
5 She isn't fifty years old. She's five years old.
6 I'm not from London. I'm from Bristol.

6 Questions and answers

Write questions and short answers.

2 Is Mr Kapoor from Uganda? Yes, he is.
3 Is Sheeba a parrot? No, she isn't.
4 Are Jack and Ananda twelve? No, they aren't.

7 WORDS A puzzle

Write the words

1 tell 2 quiet 3 laugh 4 hockey
5 who 6 please 7 form
▸ t e a c h e r
My English teacher is ...

8 Can you do this?

Write sentences with can or can't.

1 can face
2 can ball
3 can't computer
4 can draw teacher

9 What can they do?

Can or can't? Write sentences.

2 She can help in the shop.
3 He can't play hockey.
4 They can't see Prunella.
5 She can talk.
6 He can't see Polly.

10 WORDS School subjects

Find the school subjects.

	Maths	German
Geography	RE	PE
Drama	Music	Biology
History	English	Art

Now you

Look at your timetable.

2–5 It's ...

11 WORDS Where are the school words?

a) *Find and write the school words.*

▶	▼
Maths	spell
Form	subject
Music	book
timetable	Science
teacher	lessons

Fill in words from a).

2 s p e l l
3 F o r m
4 b o a r d
5 l e s s o n s
6 s u b j e c t
7 t i m e t a b l e

12 Please, Polly!

Complete the sentences.

2 don't eat 3 don't drop 4 Don't play
5 Stop Be 6 don't sing

13 WORDS Lists

Write the words in three lists.

Verbs: laugh, listen, meet, think, climb, come
Adjectives: wrong, white, clever, great
Nouns: student, marmalade, timetable, breakfast, friend

14 STUDY SKILLS Wörter lernen

a) *Im Vocabulary finde ich ...*

..., wie ich ein Wort aussprechen muss. ✓
..., wie ich ein Wort betonen muss. ✓
... Grammatikregeln.
... Paare von Gegensätzen. ✓
..., wie ich Aufsätze schreiben kann.
... nützliche Beispiele. ✓
... Hinweise auf Fehlerquellen. ✓

b) *Suche im Vocabulary*

1 student, nervous 2 wrong – right
3 mobile phone; auf Deutsch: Handy – auf Englisch: mobile phone oder mobile

15 WORDS New words

Make new words from the green words.

teacher: at, there, tree, the, he, her, here
badminton: bad, mad, on, not, at, in, it
timetable: time, table, at, eat, meet, late, it, am, me, be

16 Meet Tom and his family.

2 I've got a cat.
3 My brother has got a dog.
4 My mother has got a computer.
5 My brother and I have got a big room.

17 What have they got?

Complete with:
have got, has got, haven't got, hasn't got

have got	haven't got
hasn't got	's got
have got	has got

18 Questions and answers

Write questions with have got/has got.

2 Q: Has Ananda got a brother? A: Yes, she has.
3 Q: Has Sophie got a parrot? A: No, she hasn't.
4 Q: Have the Hansons got a B&B? A: Yes, they have.
5 Q: Have Dan and Jo got a dog?
A: No, they haven't.

Now you

Write short answers.

1 Yes, I have. / No, I haven't.
2 Yes, he has. / No, she hasn't.
3 Yes, I have. / No, I haven't.
4 Yes, he has. / No, she hasn't.

19 *Is* or *has*?

Write the sentences in the correct group.

It's nice here.	She's got a dog.
He's in Form 7PK.	Who's got a B&B?
Where's Jo?	It's got six rooms.

20 PRONUNCIATION *a* [ə] or *an* [ən]?

Write them in the correct list.

a: a yellow pen, a newspaper, a joke, a uniform, a new word
an: an apple, an old picture, an empty room, an orange bag, an exercise

21 PRONUNCIATION *the* with [ə] or [i]?

Match them to the right box.

with e: the uniform, the nice picture, the new girl
with i: the old school, the orange book, the empty house, the MP3 player, the English teacher

23 READING Meet the Baxters

b) *What's right?*

Tim	Becky	Barnabas
7SB	8JW	–
do Maths	play tennis	sit on the skateboard
Saturday	Saturday	Sunday
Science	Art	–
lots of comics	lots of posters	a pet

c) *Right or wrong? Correct the wrong sentences.*
3 Wrong. He's got lots of comics.
4 Wrong. She can't do tricks.
5 Wrong. She's thirteen.
6 Right.

24 Months of the year

Which months are they?

January	March	June	October
February	May	July	December

25 Find the month

Then find the correct month.

F	D
E	E
B	C
R	E
U	M
A	B
R	E
R	R

26 Prunella's birthday calendar

Write the dates of the birthdays.
Toby's birthday is on 3rd July.
Hannah's birthday is on 22nd October.
Sophie's birthday is on 26th March.
Sheeba's birthday is on 21st May.

Now you

My birthday is on ...
My friend's birthday is on ...

1 WORDS Tim's room

a) *Label the things in the pictures.*
1 wardrobe
2 window
3 shelf
4 bed
5 chair
6 lamp
7 desk
8 photos

b) Tim's room is picture 2.

c) 1 bathroom 2 kitchen 3 living-room
4 bedroom

2 REVISION *be*

Look at exercise 1 again. Write short answers.
Yes, it is.
No, it isn't.
Yes, he is.
No, they aren't.

3 WORDS Pets

Label the pets.
1 dog 2 horse 3 guinea pig
4 rabbit 5 hamster 6 fish
7 parrot 8 tortoise 9 budgie
10 cat 11 mouse

4 REVISION
Where the Bristol pets live

a) *What is it? Label the pictures.*
1 hutch 2 basket 3 cage

b) *What have the pets got? Write sentences.*
Bill and Ben have got a basket in the bedroom.
Hip and Hop have got a hutch in the garden.
Sheeba has got a basket in the kitchen.
Harry has got a cage in the living room.

5 PRONUNCIATION Plurals

Listen to the words.
-s kites, pets, baskets, flats, jokes,
-z windows, hands, days, lessons, numbers
-ɪz classes, tortoises, horses, pages

6 A day in the life of ...

a) *Complete with words from the box.*

get up	get up	work
have	make	
read	talk	
help	go	
meet		

b) *What's wrong with this essay?*
I get up at 7.30 in the morning. First, I wash my face and clean my teeth. Then I have breakfast in the kitchen with my mum. At school we have lessons in

Room 14. At 12.40 we all have lunch at school. After school we play football in the park. I go to bed at 9.30 in the evening.

8 -s, -es or -ies?

Write the verbs from the box in the correct lists.

-s eats, listens, sleeps
-es pushes, washes, watches
-ies tidies, tries

9 Becky's weekends

Write sentences about Becky's weekends.

2 Before lunch she goes to the shops.
3 In the afternoon she plays tennis in the park.
4 In the evening she watches TV with her family.
5 On Sunday she helps her mum in the kitchen.

10 Sundays

a) I/You/We/Lots of boys and girls eat lots of toast; like Sundays; watch TV; go to places; have a big breakfast
My friend has a small breakfast; reads comics; goes to the park; eats toast; likes Sundays; listen to music.

b) *Complete Sophie's text.*

eats	likes
go	goes
help	watches
reads	sleep
talks	listen
watch	like

11 WORDS Find the right word

Match two fish, colour the fish, then write one new word.
weekend, breakfast, sometimes, homework, afternoon, birthday, bedroom

12 Right or wrong?

Mark the sentences right (√) or wrong (x).

3 ✓
4 ✗ Hamsters don't like marmalade.
5 ✗ Rabbits don't eat fish.
6 ✗ Dogs don't go to school.
7 ✗ Cats don't drink tea.
8 ✓

13 We're all different

a) 1 My mum doesn't like dogs. 2 My dad … . 3 … 4 … 5 … 6 …

b) 1 doesn't 2 don't 3 doesn't 4 don't 5 doesn't 6 don't 7 doesn't 8 doesn't

14 What Prunella does

Write about Prunella.

3 She drops things. 4 She doesn't sleep.
5 She sings songs.
6 She opens and closes things.
7 She doesn't go to the shops.
8 She laughs.
9 She doesn't go to school.
10 She watches and thinks.
11 She doesn't talk to Emily.
12 She pushes and pulls things.

15 WORDS Family words

Put the family words from the box in the right list.

mother	father
aunt	uncle
daughter	son
sister	brother
grandma	grandpa

16 Who are they?

a) *Look at the Baxters' family tree. Who's who?*

2 b) Dave and Cathy's son.
3 a) Tim and Becky's cousin.
c) Kate and Simon's daughter.
4 a) Lucy's aunt.
b) Tim and Becky's mother.
5 c) Dave and Kate's mother.

b) *Now complete what Tim says about his family.*

aunt's cousin's
parents'
grandparents'

17 What's wrong?

Write the sentences again.
The Thompsons, Jo and Dan's grandparents, are at the Shaws' house. Dan and Jo's mum is the Thompsons' daughter Catherine. Dan's favourite uncle is Catherine's brother Harry. Dan and Jo have got three cousins too. Anne is Dan's favourite cousin, and Mark is Jo's favourite cousin.

18 Our pet photos

Complete with: my, your, his, her, its, our, your, their

1 my Her
2 its
3 my/our their his
4 your
5 my/our her
6 Your its

19 READING Tim's Saturday

a) *Look at the pictures. Then read the texts. Match the texts to the pictures.*

1 C 2 D 3 B 4 A

b) *What goes together?*

A The end of the day
B Lunch in the park
C Breakfast with the family
D A great place for a good time

1 WORDS Sports and hobbies

Write lists of Form 7PK's sports and hobbies.

Sports	Hobbies
go swimming	collect stamps
play hockey	make models
go riding	play the guitar

2 REVISION Sophie goes riding ...

Complete the sentences.

2	goes	doesn't go
3	makes	doesn't play
4	go	don't go
5	play	don't collect

3 WORDS A picture puzzle

a) *Complete the picture puzzle.*

1 d r e s s
2 b o o t s
3 s h o e s
4 s h o r t s
5 s o c k s
6 j e a n s
7 T – s h i r t

b) *Now complete the sentences about Florian with words from a).*

T-shirt
boots
socks
shorts

4 Do you play ...?

Write questions.

1 Yes, I do. / No, I don't.
2 play tennis
Yes, I do. / No, I don't.
3 you play basketball
Yes, I do. / No, I don't.
4 Do you play hockey?
Yes, I do. / No, I don't.
5 Do you play table tennis?
Yes, I do. / No, I don't.

5 Weekends

Write questions.

2 listen to music
3 you play the guitar
4 Do you meet your friends?
5 Do you read comics in bed?

6 Ananda's hockey shoes

Complete the questions with do or does.

2		they do
3	Does	it does
4	Does	she doesn't
5	Does	she does
6	Do	they don't

7 Free time

Write questions.

2 Does Sophie collect plates?
3 Do Dan and Jo go swimming?
4 Does Prunella play hockey?
5 Do Dan and Jo make models?

8 What does Ananda ask?

Complete her questions with: What, When, Who, Where

2 Where 3 When
4 What 5 Who

9 STUDY SKILLS Wörter nachschlagen

a) *The boxes are full of Sophie's old things. Write the words in alphabetical order.*

birthday cards	computer games
books	packets of stamps
boxes	photos
calendars	pictures
CDs	posters

b) *Add the following words to the list of p-words.*

pencils, pens, photos, pictures, poems, posters

10 PRONUNCIATION [æ] and [eɪ]

Listen to the words.

æ *flat, bag, rabbit, black, back, stamp, act, plan, lamp*
eɪ *plate, day, late, make, table, say, place*

11 Sentence snakes

Cross out the wrong word. Then write the sentence.

2 Prunella never sleeps.
3 Becky often plays tennis.
4 Emily can never find her bag.
5 Tim doesn't usually get up early.
6 Jack always writes great stories.

12 About Tim

Write sentences about Tim.

2 He sometimes makes breakfast.
3 He always goes to football matches.
4 He never gets up before 7 o'clock.
5 He usually watches TV after school.
6 He often goes to bed late.

13 WORDS *Go, play* or *do?*

a) *Match, then write.*

go go dancing, go riding
play hockey, play basketball, play badminton, play tennis
do judo, do yoga

b) *Now complete Toby's sentences with the correct form of go, play or do.*

play do
plays goes go
does

14 WORDS Pairs

a) *Which words go together?*

		alone	– together
never	– always	teach	– learn
ask	– answer	married	– divorced
difficult	– easy	upstairs	– downstairs

b) *Complete with words from a).*

always never
after
upstairs Downstairs
easy difficult

15 Who has to do what?

Write sentences with have to, has to, don't have to or doesn't have to.

2 Tim has to clean his bike.
3 Becky and Tim have to clean the kitchen.
4 Becky doesn't have to go to her piano lesson.
5 Tim and Becky don't have to get up early.
6 Florian doesn't have to make his bed.

16 WORKING WITH THE TEXT The SHoCK Team

a) *Match the text to the pictures.*

1 B 2 D 3 A
4 C 5 F 6 E

b) *Who thinks what?*

Ananda Jack has to tell his parents about the man in black.
Jack We all have to watch Mr Green.
Dan Jack has to call the police.
I've got a piece of paper. Here it is.
Jo Yes! 'Detective Jo Shaw'...

c) *Write answers.*

1 No, he doesn't.
2 Jack thinks he is a spy or a bank robber.
3 They have to find out about Mr Green. / They have to be detectives.

d) *In the History lesson, Jack writes a code message to the SHoCK Team. What does it say?*

W H E R E D O E S
M R G R E E N G O
A F T E R
B R E A K F A S T ?
W E H A V E T O
F I N D O U T !

17 In the Oxfam shop

a) *How much is it?*

70p £5.00 £3.49 £2.85 £2.60 £6.50 £10.99

b) *Jo is in the Oxfam shop. What does Jo say?*

J	J
A	A
A	J
A	A
J	J

2 Yes, how much is the skateboard, please?
3 Let's see. It's £10.99.
4 Oh, that's too much. How much is the bag?
5 The bag is £6.50.
6 Mmm. I've only got £6.50 and 25p is for the bus.
7 Mmm. Well, I can take 25p off.
8 Oh, then I'll take it. Here's the money.
9 And here's your change. Thank you.
10 Thank you. Bye.

1 WORDS Sophie's shopping list

a) *Write Sophie's shopping list of food and drinks for the party*

1 cheese	8 biscuits
2 chicken	9 crips
3 sweets	10 fruit
4 sausages	11 chips
5 chocolate cake	12 lemonade
6 carrots	13 cola
7 ice cream	14 orange juice

Unit 4

2 WORDS What's on the table?

Match words from the boxes.

2 a jug of milk
3 a bowl of cornflakes
4 a bottle of orange juice
5 a basket of fruit

3 Would you like some tea?

Complete Becky's questions and Florian's answers.

2 'd like some orange juice
3 you like some biscuits
4 thank you I'd like some chocolate cake

4 An invitation

What does the invitation say?

Dear
Please to
Where
On
At

5 Sophie's party

a) *Match and colour.*

he – him
she – her
it – it
we – us
you – you
they – them

b) *Now complete with: me, you, him, her, it, us, them*

1 them
2 me it
3 you
4 him us her

6 Invitations

Find and circle the correct word.

1 it
2 them her
3 them

7 STUDY SKILLS Notizen machen

Mark the key words, then write them.

Dan – photos of Mr Green
Ananda – find out – bank robbers – computer
Jack – follow – on bike – Sunday
Dan – all meet – Sunday evening
Jack – meet – park at 6

8 WORDS The mad computer

a) *The mad computer sometimes writes wrong letters. Write the words with the correct letters.*

invitation funny expensive boring
present sunglasses difficult

b) *Now put the correct words from a) in Ananda's e-mail to Jack.*

invitation
present expensive
funny difficult
boring
sunglasses

9 Some sausages and some milk

a) *What have Tim and Becky got in their baskets?*

Becky: cheese, some biscuits, some chocolate
Tim: some ice cream, some lemonade, some crisps

b) *Which three things haven't they got?*

any corrots, any fruit, any sausages

10 Tim's birthday list

What does Tim want for his birthday?

2 some any hockey shoes
3 any socks some money
4 any
5 any other sweets

11 At the Baxters'

What are the Baxters doing? Make sentences.

2 the cooker
3 Mr Baxter is tidying the living room.
4 Grandma and Grandpa are watching TV.
5 Tim and Florian are making a mess.
6 Becky and Lucy are playing a computer game.

12 Where are the verbs?

a) *Find and write nine verbs.*

run write give get
walk follow swim take

b) *Now write the verbs in the correct list.*

walk – walking write – writing run – running
follow – following give – giving get – getting

13 Becky's dream birthday

Becky is thinking about her dream birthday.

're eating 're drinking
are giving
is playing
'm dancing
is sitting 's talking
are swimming
are singing

14 Prunella's visitor

Write two sentences for each picture.

2 He isn't watching TV. He's listening to music.
3 They aren't reading newspapers.
They're looking at old photos.
4 She isn't dancing. She's playing the piano.
5 They aren't eating ice cream.
They're having sandwiches and tea.

15 Questions and answers

Write questions.

1 Is Uncle Henry reading newspapers? No, he isn't.
2 Are Prunella and Uncle Henry having sandwiches and tea? Yes, they are.
3 Is Prunella playing the piano? Yes, she is.

16 PRONUNCIATION [əʊ] or [ɒ]

Listen to the words.

əʊ poster, home, old, yoga, bowl, boat,
ɒ clock, hockey, hobby, comic, box

17 WORDS Where are the body words?

▶	▼
hair	face
eye	fingers
leg	arm
hand	feet
mouth	toes
foot	nose
knee	

18 READING Tim's party

a) *Read about Tim's birthday party.*
Write the names of his friends in the picture.

Florian, Lucy, Pat, Ali, Gina, Tim, Sue, Jill, Alex, Ed

b) *Now complete the sentences.*

1 his 12th birthday
2 he's hiding
3 presents and lots of food
4 jeans and a nice red T-shirt
5 is telling funny jokes
6 isn't playing (it)
7 fish, chicken and sausages

1 WORDS Happy birthday, Grandpa

Which words can't Jo's grandpa read? Write the words.

practise, Choir, pirates, Computer, programmes, paint, ship, rehearsal, results

2 WORDS School notice board

Write the correct names. Then find the missing club.

2 Football Team
3 Junior Band
4 Dance Club
5 Junior Choir
6 Art Club

3 An e-mail from Becky

Here is an e-mail from Becky to her friend Lisa. Fill in was or were.

was
were were
was
were were Were
Was

4 Where were Tim's things?

Write sentences about Tim's things with was, wasn't, were and weren't.

2 His football wasn't — It was
3 His comics weren't — They were
4 His clock wasn't — It was
5 His school things weren't — They were
6 wasn't — was in Tim's bed

5 Saturday afternoon

Write questions with was or were and short answers.

3 Was Jack at the pet shop? – Yes, he was.
4 Were Tim and Florian at a football match? – Yes, they were.
5 Was Ananda at the café? – No, she wasn't. She was at the sports shop.
6 Were Becky and Lucy at home? – No, they weren't. They were at the café.

6 WORDS What are the words?

a) *Find and write the missing letters.*

sh ou t — n oi se — bec au se
w ai t — r ea dy — n ei ghb ou r
p eo ple — s ou nd — with ou t
ch oi r — upst ai rs

b) *Now fill in correct forms from a).*

rehearsal — without
sound wait
people — neighbours — choir
noise

Unit 5

7 A verb snake

Find and colour the verbs in the verb snake. Then write them in the simple past.

helped, listened, talked, watched, asked, walked, waited

8 PRONUNCIATION Word CDs

a) *Listen to the words. Where can you hear the extra syllable –ed [id]? Colour the CDs red or blue.*

red: painted, added, waited, shouted, started, hated

9 Last week

Look at Tim's notes for last week. Then write sentences.

walked to school
Wednesday he helped Alex with Maths.
On Thursday he called Florian and Ed.
On Friday he watched DVDs with Florian.
On Saturday he played cards with Ed.

10 Match the pieces

a) *Find, colour and write the pairs.*

Infinitive	Simple past
go	went
do	did
see	saw
say	said
come	came

b) *Now complete the story about Tim with verbs from a).*

had	went
said	
went/came	had
said	said
went	

11 REVISION He doesn't do that

Complete the sentences about Barnabas.

doesn't eat	doesn't take
doesn't make	
don't bring	
don't sleep	

12 They didn't do that ...

Complete the sentences.

1	didn't play	
2	didn't listen	didn't call
3	didn't watch	didn't write

13 The Spring Show

Complete the sentences with simple past forms.

2	said	looked
3	didn't sing	danced
4	came	
5	didn't see	
6	wasn't	was

14 Questions and answers

Match the questions and answers. Then write the correct blue letter: t i c k e t

2	Were all the kids nervous?	Yes, they were.
3	Did Sophie dance in the show?	Yes, she did.
4	Did Jack and Ananda sing?	No, they didn't.
5	Was Prunella at the show?	No, she wasn't.
6	Did Jo play in the band?	No, he didn't.

15 WORDS What's wrong?

Look at the boxes and write the correct words in the puzzle. Then find the word down.

m	a	g	a	z	i	n	e			
i	n	f	o	r	m	a	t	i	o	n
s	p	y								
t	i	r	e	d						
a	r	t	i	c	l	e				
k	i	n	g							
e	x	a	m	p	l	e				

16 STUDY SKILLS Unbekannte Wörter verstehen

b) *Wie kannst du diese Wörter erschließen? Setze Häkchen (✓):*

mask	✓	✓	
strict			✓
ugly	✓		✓

c) *Schreib drei Wörter auf, die du durch die Bilder erschließen kannst.*

mask (Maske), beautiful (schön)

d) *Schreib fünf Wörter auf, die im Deutschen ähnlich sind. Schreib auch das deutsche Wort auf.*

opera (Oper), tragic (tragisch), mysterious (mysteriös), genius (Genie), wonderful (wundervoll), singer (Sänger/-in), romantic (romantisch), angel (Engel)

e) *Welche Wörter kannst du aus dem Zusammenhang erschließen?*

ugly (hässlich), ghost (Gespenst)

17 WORKING WITH THE TEXT A pirate story

a) *Match the pictures and the titles A–D.*

1 B 2 D
3 A 4 C

b) *What's wrong? Mark the wrong sentences and correct them.*

1 from the Silver Swordfish were on the ship
2 to kill the sailors on the ship
3 'Bad luck for you, boy
4 on the floor of his room

c) *Now you are Jo. Tell Dan about your dream in the simple past. Use the notes or your own ideas.*

First the Captain and Bonny killed two sailors on the Silver Swordfish. In the cabin I saw that Bonny was a woman. After that the pirates wanted to kill me. I was on the plank!

1 WORDS Places to go

a) *Where did Florian and his cousin go? Fill in the missing words from the box.*

village
station
café museum
church
tower park
bridge
café

2 WORDS Word bridges

a) *How many words can you make from the word bridges?*

c – e: cake, come, change, cheese, chocolate, choose, classmate, close, centre, comfortable, costume
h – e: have, hate, here, hole, home, hide, house he, hope
e – e: exercise, expensive, example, explore everywhere, excuse

3 What are they going to do?

Match and write sentence pairs.

Jack's homework is boring. He's going to read a spy story.

Jo and Dan are hungry. They're going to make some sandwiches.

Tim and Florian like football. They're going to watch a match on TV.

Barnabas is tired. He's going to sleep on the sofa.

4 REVISION No, you didn't, Prunella!

What does Sophie say? Write her sentences.

1 watch TV every evening
2 didn't have an MP3 player
3 You didn't play computer games
4 you didn't collect phone cards
5 you didn't go to judo lessons

5 Sophie likes the library because ...

a) *Match and write correct sentences with because or when.*

2 Dan hates it when Jo sings the pirate song.
3 Prunella doesn't get up late because she doesn't sleep.
4 Ananda doesn't like it when people argue.

b) *Now write sentences about Barnabas with the words in the correct order.*

1 is always happy when Tim feeds him
2 Tim hates it when Barnabas sits on his face.
3 The neighbour throws water at Barnabas because he doesn't like cats in his garden.

6 WORDS Good and bad words

a) *Which are good words? Write them in green. Which are bad words? Write them in red.*

green easy, fun, great, happy, interesting, pretty, smile,
red boring, danger, dead, difficult, poor, scary, terrible

7 These aren't my things

What does Jo say about his things? Use this, that, these, those.

2 This isn't my T-shirt. That's my T-shirt
3 my shoes. Those are my shoes
4 This isn't my skateboard. That's my skateboard
5 These aren't my socks. Those are my socks
6 These aren't my comics. Those are my comics

8 PRONUNCIATION [ʃ], [tʃ] and [dʒ]

Listen to the CD and colour the words.

1 information [ʃ] – juice [dʒ]
2 check [tʃ] – finish [ʃ]
3 village [dʒ] – chicken [tʃ]
4 church [tʃ] – Geography [dʒ]
5 bridge [dʒ] – shout [ʃ]
6 chair [tʃ] – chocolate [tʃ]

9 REVISION A scary story?

a) *Complete the sentences. Use the simple present.*

Tim *have got*
often hears
says *sometimes makes*
often sees
Florian *does he do*
does he go *Does he drop*
Tim *doesn't do* *always goes*
eats *don't eat*
think *is*

10 REVISION A school trip

Lucy is on a school trip. She writes to her family. Use these verbs in the present progressive: have, sit, wear, swim, play, take, talk

are playing
is sitting
are talking
is wearing
's taking
're having

11 What's different?

Today is different. What do the students and teachers usually do? What are they doing today? Circle the correct verb form.

has
are playing *does*
are singing *listen*
aren't listening *are making*
eat *are eating* *are having*
isn't shouting

12 Who's who?

a) *Write the verbs in the simple present or present progressive.*

doesn't read *usually buys*
is wearing *is eating*
likes *is reading*
doesn't like

b) *Who's who? Write their names.*

2 *Liz* 3 *Sally* 4 *Sarah* 5 *Jane*

13 REVISION *There, their or they're*

Dan *They're* *there*
Jo *their* *there*
Dan *They're*

14 WORDS A puzzle

a) *Complete the sentences.*

2 v i l l a g e
3 o n e m o r e
4 w h i s p e r
5 f i n i s h

b) The word is: s m i l e .

15 REVISION Getting by in English

You meet the English girl, Jenny, on the street. Ask her questions in English.

How old are you?
Do you like sport?
Does your brother like sport?
Have you got a pet?
Do you play the guitar?
Who is your favourite band?
Would you like to listen to my CDs?
Would you like to go to a party with me on Friday?